Welcome to Group

Words We Use for Worry

Contact Information

Name: _____

e-mail: _____

Home telephone: _____

Cell phone: _____

Work telephone: _____

My food allergies, if any (snack will be served during group):

_____

_____

My child's food allergies, if any (snack will be served during group):

_____

_____

Brainstorming Goals!

My goals for group:	My goals for my child for group:
1.	1.
2.	2.
3.	3.
4.	4.
5.	5.

Reinforcer Assessment

List the things that your child really enjoys under each category. Then, highlight the top 5 items/activities across categories that may motivate your child the most.

Foods and/or Drinks	Toys/Games	Objects	Activities	People Your Child Enjoys

These may include video and electronic games, stuffed animals, movies, and so forth.

These may include sensory materials, household items, and so forth.

These may include outdoor activities or games (e.g., jumping on the trampoline), sensory activities (e.g., bath), and so forth.

Below is a **Words for Worry Word Search** worksheet that your child will complete before the next session. This should be a fun exercise that helps increase your child's vocabulary to describe symptoms of anxiety and worry.

SESSION 1

Words for Worry Word Search

Everyone talks about worry in different ways.
Find the 12 words below that describe how people feel
when they are worried.

```
D O V E R W H E L M E D E F T
F E A M G R D L P S C I T R W
E R I T U P S E T B H Z J I O
A T C E Z H C G M W E H M G T
R S O T S I N E R V O U S H O
F C M D B K C P B E R E A T F
U A F E V A F R A I D L G E J
L R Q H L R N I P G V Q R N A
C E M W K T F X K W P Z A E G
B D H O F S D B I T S Z T D I
L B Y R A G T O V O E F L Y T
R K E R B H Z M W R U A M I A
A G F Y Y E C S K N L S J W T
L M R G J K W J E T R Q K C E
F R E A K E D O U T O U E T D
```

WORRY	SCARED	UPSET	FREAKED OUT
AFRAID	FRIGHTENED	ANXIOUS	MELTDOWN
NERVOUS	FEARFUL	AGITATED	OVERWHELMED

Did you find all the words?
What words do you use to describe how you feel sometimes?

Session Notes

When I Worry

Intervention Overview

Below, you will see a brief summary of the treatment approach for anxiety and what the main topics are for discussion in the upcoming weeks. This treatment overview may look rather intimidating at first; keep in mind, however, that we will be reviewing and discussing these concepts repeatedly throughout the group sessions.

1. Identify symptoms of anxiety and situations or things that make your child anxious.

    *   By identifying the variety of symptoms of anxiety your child displays when he or she is worried or fearful, you are teaching self-awareness of symptoms and behaviors. Later, when you observe these behaviors, you can coach your child to use the coping strategies and tools practiced in group sessions.

    *   By identifying the situations that make your child anxious or the objects, places, or people that your child avoids, you will be able to get a sense of what contributes to your child's anxiety as well as how much these symptoms affect your lives. The identification of these situations also will become the foundation for creating exposure hierarchies, or in other words, facing fears gradually (see number 6).

2. Establish a context for thinking about anxiety.

    *   Physical reactions to anxiety: Anxiety is a problem of overreactivity. When you sense or feel real danger, such as when you are in a burning building, your body goes into action—fight, flight, or freeze. Some people's bodies, however, overreact to lots of different situations, signaling danger when there is no real danger. Physical reactions such as dry mouth, rapid heart rate, and sweaty palms may continue despite the "false alarm." Self-awareness of these "false alarms" will be emphasized along with strategies to reduce the body's physical reaction as well as to change your child's beliefs about the event.

    *   Externalize anxiety: You and your child, together with the group facilitators, will fight his or her anxiety symptoms. The children will create "worry bugs" to represent worry or fear. The children will then identify friends and family members on their team who will help them beat anxiety. Your child's success depends on our joint efforts!

3. Introduce tools or strategies to fight or resist anxiety symptoms.

    *   Get a handle on the body's physical reaction: Work to decrease anxiety with deep breathing or by engaging in other calming activities. Your child will practice measuring and monitoring anxiety symptoms in a regular way; as the children increase awareness of anxiety symptoms and corresponding strategies for relaxing or calming themselves, they are developing skills to improve emotion regulation.

    *   Pay attention to "active minds" or thoughts that tend to occur when your child is worried or fearful, and help your child generate "helpful" thoughts instead.

    *   Encourage a plan for self-evaluation and/or self-reward.

4. Identify and teach necessary social skills.

    *   There is not a specific social skills module included in this intervention package, but opportunities to identify and teach social skills occur throughout each session. In addition, if it appears as though social skills deficits may be exacerbating your child's anxiety in a particular situation, the necessary social skills will be taught through role play and scripting, along with graded exposure techniques.

(continued)

(continued)
Intervention Overview

5. Determine your child's steps to success.

   - You and your child will list many of the objects, places, or people that make your child anxious and rank order them based on how much anxiety they produce and/or how much they interfere with your child's quality of life. You will then select a starting point and work to gradually have your child face his or her fears.

6. Help your child make a plan to face his or her fears.

   - Choose a reasonable, low-intensity target.

   - Identify tools and/or strategies that your child finds most effective in reducing anxiety symptoms.

   - Practice during group sessions and at home, gradually facing fears (exposure hierarchy).

7. Encourage self-evaluation and self-reward as a final step in facing fears.

   - Teach your child to evaluate his or her own behavior. Rate his or her effort in handling anxiety-producing situations and identify strategies for what he or she could do differently the next time. Parents may reward children for their effort in facing fears, and children ultimately can be taught to reward themselves.

8. Prevent relapse of symptoms by reviewing and practicing coping techniques, establishing plans for handling future symptoms, and taking home the *Facing Your Fears* group videos made by the children.

9. Try these additional recommendations (Barrett et al., 2004; Cobham et al., 1998; Mendlowitz et al., 1999).

   - Encourage and reward your child for his or her effort and engagement in brave behaviors.

   - Ignore excessive displays of anxiety.

   - Make the connection between anxious thoughts, physical changes your child may experience, and anxious behaviors.

   - Convey confidence in your child's ability to handle his or her worry and/or anxiety.

   - Model your own courageous behaviors.

   - Be aware of your parenting style and/or any personal anxiety issues that may affect your child's ability to face fears.

   - Work together with your spouse and/or partner to develop a plan.

   - Remember, we may learn best from the mistakes we make (Kendall & Hedtke, 2006).

Session Notes

Time Spent Worrying

Things I Like to Do to Relax

We all engage in a number of different relaxing or calming activities in our day-to-day lives. Sometimes, these activities help us calm down when we are feeling particularly stressed or anxious. Today, we will spend a little time sharing some of these ideas. Your child just learned about several children and how much time they spend worrying. With these activities fresh in your mind, you may better be able to help your child generate some calming and/or relaxing activities that might work for him or her on a daily basis when he or she is feeling stressed or anxious. First, take a little time to jot down some things you do to relax on this form.

_____

_____

_____

_____

_____

_____

_____

_____

_____

_____

_____

_____

_____

_____

_____

Below are several worksheets your child will complete in group that will help him or her externalize anxiety symptoms.

Next, you are going to create several characters. Your first character is your WORRY BUG. Almost everyone has a worry bug. Worry bugs are the fears and anxiety that get in our way and make it hard for us to learn in school, have fun at home, or play with friends.

What does your worry bug look like?
What will you call it?

Once you have drawn or created your worry bug on the next page, draw or create your HELPER BUG. A helper bug is an imaginary creature that helps you defeat your worry bug!

What does your helper bug look like?
What will you call it?

Next, on the **My Team to Help Beat Worry** worksheet, write the names of all of the friends, family members, or fictional characters that can help you beat worry!

Finally, create something (either with Play-Doh or markers) that shows you and your helper bug squashing your worry bug!

My Team to Help Beat Worry

Squashing My Worry Bug!

Session Notes

_____

_____

_____

_____

_____

_____

_____

_____

_____

_____

_____

_____

_____

_____

_____

_____

_____

_____

_____

_____

_____

_____

What Worry Does to My Body

Beginning to Measure Worry

On the picture below, circle or color how worry makes *your* body feel. For example, if worrying makes your stomach upset, circle or color the butterflies on the boy's stomach.

What does worry do to your body?

What Worry Does to Your Body

Progressive Muscle Relaxation Script

The following is a script you can use when working with your child to help him or her relax. Note: Before beginning the relaxation exercise, isolate and practice with your child each of the following muscle movements: 1) squeeze arms and hands tightly; 2) squeeze legs tightly, toes flat; 3) tense face muscles; 4) squeeze stomach muscles; and 5) tense the whole body. Then, have your child identify a special calming place that you can describe when you get to the "visualization" portion of the script.

GETTING COMFORTABLE (At this point, the parent begins to read the script to the child.)

Go ahead and settle back so you feel comfortable. Let all of your muscles go loose and heavy. Close your eyes and take three deep, slow breaths. As you breathe in slowly, concentrate on the air as it fills your lungs; and as you breathe out slowly, notice your breath rushing out through your nose and mouth. Breathe slowly, thinking about the feeling of air passing in (pause) and out of your body (pause).

Arms and Hands

Now, pretend you have a whole lemon in each of your hands. Squeeze the lemons as hard as you can—try to squeeze all of the juice out. While you're squeezing both hands, make a muscle with your upper arms as well so that your arms and hands are tight and squeezed. Hold that tight feeling in your arms as I begin to count.... 5...4...3...2...1.... Now, drop the lemon and relax your fist and arm. Notice the feelings of warmth and relaxation that flow through your fingers into your hands and arms. Now, squeeze those lemons again as hard as you can. Feel the muscles in your hands, lower arms, and upper arms tighten and squeeze. Hold that tight feeling in your arms as I count.... 5...4...3...2...1...relax. Notice how the tight feeling leaves your arms and is replaced by the warm, heavy feelings of relaxation (pause).

Legs

Now, squeeze your legs as tight as you can, make a muscle in your upper leg and lower leg, and curl your toes as tight as you can so that your whole legs on both sides are tight and squeezed. Hold that tightness while I count.... 5...4...3...2...1.... Let the tightness in your legs go loose (pause). Do it again.

(continued)

(continued)
Progressive Muscle Relaxation Script

Face

Now I want you to scrunch up your face like you just bit into something really sour, like a lemon. Wrinkle up your forehead, your nose, your mouth, and your cheeks; squeeze your eyes shut as tight as you can.... 5...4...3...2...1.... Now, relax (pause); smooth out all the wrinkles in your forehead, nose, mouth, cheeks, and eyes.... Breathe deeply as you notice the warm, heavy feelings of relaxation in your body. Do it again.

Stomach

Now, pretend you're lying on your back and an elephant is about to step on your stomach. Tighten up your stomach muscles harder and harder, and pay attention to your stomach muscles as I count down.... 5...4...3...2...1.... Relax your stomach muscles and feel how warm, heavy, and relaxed your stomach feels.

Whole Body

Now, I want you to tighten your whole body, from your scrunched up face to your hunched shoulders, your tight fists and arms, your stiff back and stomach, and your tight legs and curled toes. Make your whole body stiff as a board and hold it as I count.... 5...4...3...2...1.... Let go and relax (pause). Just relax and feel how warm and heavy your whole body feels. Relax.

Visualization

With your eyes closed, I want you to imagine that you're in a forest.... (Describe the place; focus on the sensory details such as the warmth or coolness of the air, the soft sounds in the background, the sunlight on your face, the smell of the earth and pine trees.) Now it's time to leave your special place and come back to this room. We're going to take five imaginary steps, each step moving farther away from the forest and closer to this room. I'll count each step out for you. 5...You're stepping away from your special place.... 4...You've moved a little farther away from the forest.... 3...You're half way back to this room.... 2... You're almost here, just one small step away.... 1...And you're back. When you feel ready, go ahead and open your eyes.

Relaxation Practice at Home—Tips!

The practice of relaxation is one of the most basic anxiety-reducing techniques. For some children, physical relaxation (e.g., deep breathing) works best for calming; for others, relaxing the mind is most helpful. Whatever strategy your child chooses as his preferred approach, he will need to practice. Sound easy? In theory, it is. However, the ability to relax in daily life requires learning and practice. Below you will find three common approaches to relaxation that you can practice at home with your child. Which one works best for him? Which one does he like doing?

 Deep breathing: Have your child sit up in a chair in a comfortable position wearing loose clothing. Encourage her to breathe in slowly to a count of 5; then, slowly exhale, making sure that the exhale is longer than the inhale. After your child has practiced a few times, have your child place her hand on her stomach and ask your child to make her stomach move out as she breathes in deeply (e.g., "Blow up your tummy like a beach ball"). Repeat the inhalation, hold breath, and exhalation sequence a number of times. Sometimes, children like to practice deep breathing right before they go to sleep.

 Body mindfulness: Have your child practice experiencing the difference between being tense and tight and relaxed and loose. Pretend to be a robot. Walk around the room with stiff legs, arms, and body. Talk about what it feels like. Then, flop down in a chair like a wet noodle. Talk about what it feels like in your body to be floppy and droopy like a wet noodle. During the day, if you notice that your child is stiff and tense, remind him about the robot and wet noodle. How can he get his body to be more relaxed like a wet noodle? Learning to distinguish between a relaxed and a tense state is an important skill for your child to develop.

 Using self-talk: Positive self-talk can be helpful for some children. Brainstorm with your child about some helpful sayings that might work for her (e.g., "I can beat my worries," "Just breathe, I can do it!"). When your child has selected a saying, have her practice with deep breathing. For other children, particularly children with intense special interests or preoccupations, (e.g., animals, movies, video games), it may be calming to think about their favorite interests as a way to calm down. For example, listing favorite animals or characters may be a useful strategy for some children when upset.

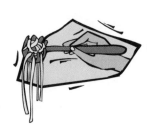 Remember, the goal of relaxation is to bring your baseline level of arousal down to a lower level. All of these coping techniques work best when anxiety is not yet severe. Try them out during everyday activities, such as when your child just wakes up in the morning, before he heads off to school, or when he is beginning to become a little overaroused.

GOOD LUCK TRYING THESE OUT! WE LOOK FORWARD TO HEARING HOW IT GOES.

Schedule for Calming and/or Relaxing Activities

Calming Activities	Sunday	Monday	Tuesday	Wednesday	Thursday	Friday	Saturday
1.							
2.							
3.							
4.							
5.							
6.							
7.							
8.							

Reward Plan:

Completing 1–2 activities per week = _____

Completing 3–4 activities per week = _____

Completing 5–6+ activities per week = _____

Session Notes

The Mind–Body Connection

Below are several worksheets that will help your child understand "active minds" and "helpful thoughts."

Below, you will meet Matthew, who is afraid of snakes. When he goes to the zoo and sees a snake, his mind becomes very active, he begins to think a lot about the snake, and he worries about what might happen.

How will Matthew's body feel when he thinks these thoughts?

Take a look and see!

What do you think?

SESSION 5

Active Minds

At the zoo one day . . .

I can't look at the snake! It's so scary!

Uh oh. It's going to get out of its cage.

I have to get out of here!

What if it escapes and comes to my house?

I'm never going to the zoo again!

It's going to kill me! Oh no, maybe it will kill my mom!

What if there are snakes in my backyard? I can't play ball!

A snake in a cage at the Snake House

Will thinking these thoughts make him feel better or worse?

Below, see if you can help Matthew. Write down what the boy might think or say to help his body feel less anxious when he sees the snake.

How will Matthew's body feel when he thinks these thoughts?

What do you think?

Suggestions for Helpful Thoughts

"This is just a 'false alarm.'"

"I can face my fear; nothing bad will happen."

"The worry feelings will go away."

"I can handle this."

"This is no big deal."

"It's my worry bug; I can squash it!"

"I can fight back with facts."

Fight back with facts:

The glass cage is very thick.

Snakes hardly ever escape from cages.

The snake does not know where I live.

Now it's your turn! Think about a situation that makes you feel really anxious or worried. For example, maybe you feel really anxious when you hear thunder.

On the next page, write down the situation in the space at the top of the **Active Minds** worksheet.

Next, think about how your body feels and what happens when your mind becomes active. What does your ACTIVE MIND say? What are you thinking during this situation? Will thinking these thoughts make your body feel better or worse?

Write down how your body feels and what your thoughts are in the thought bubbles.

Active Minds

One day _____

**Will thinking these thoughts
make you feel better or worse?**

Now, think of some helpful thoughts that would make you feel better in this situation.

How will your body feel if you think helpful thoughts?

Write your helpful thoughts down on the next page!

Helpful Thoughts

One day _____

**Will thinking these thoughts
make you feel better or worse?**

Plan to Get to Green

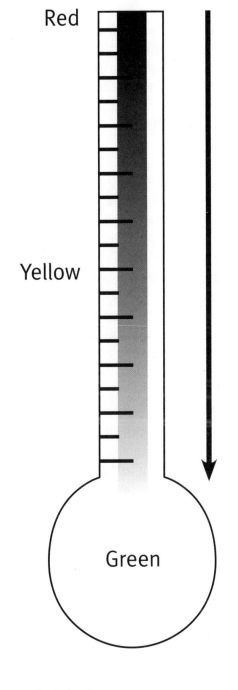

Red

Yellow

Green

Helpful Hints

What helps the most
when my child is in red?

What makes things worse?

Managing active minds ("false alarm"):

Helpful thoughts _____

Fight fears with facts _____

_____

Managing the body's reaction:

Deep breathing _____

_____

_____

Rewards for moving from red to yellow
and from yellow to green:

_____

_____

Rewards for staying in green:

_____

_____

Cycle of Anxiety

We will be reviewing the cycle of anxiety today. The handout **Anxiety Components: A Fearful Experience at the Zoo** illustrates how the body's physical reactions to a feared situation lead to increased thoughts of danger, which then lead to avoidance of the fearful situation. This cycle of behavior ultimately results in fewer opportunities to practice coping skills and increases perceptions of danger. Your child will be introduced to this concept through the story of Matthew. We'll use the example of Matthew's trip to the zoo to illustrate the cycle of anxiety.

We will then discuss the concepts of adaptive and excessive protection. *Adaptive protection* is a functional parenting style that may occur when children have marked areas of developmental, physical, or emotional challenges. For example, children with extensive challenges may experience "realistic" fears in their everyday lives, and as a result, parents must carefully limit their children's exposure to challenging events to create multiple success experiences for them over time. Excessive protection, however, is a parenting style that may limit the child's exposure to anxiety-producing situations even though the child may possess the necessary developmental skills to be successful in the situation. The parent's efforts are directed at unnecessarily protecting the child from fearful situations by avoiding the situation altogether. As a result, the child may not learn the coping skills necessary to later face this situation.

The **Anxiety/Exposure Graph** visually displays the fact that individuals can habituate or get used to worry and/or anxiety over time. When an individual is in a stressful situation and then leaves, anxiety drops quickly. This can teach individuals that fleeing an anxiety-producing situation is the fastest way to reduce anxious feelings. Remaining in the anxiety-producing situation may seem counterintuitive. However, staying in the anxious situation over time is truly the most effective way to handle anxiety; by remaining in the situation long enough, children will gain the awareness and experience that anxious feelings can become less intense over time. Children need the opportunity to get used to anxious feelings and see that they can be manageable.

We will then discuss the difference between realistic and unrealistic fears by completing a series of worksheets about a boy named Frank **(Frank's Fears)**. The difference between realistic fear and unrealistic fear (i.e., "false alarms") is important, because this distinction will guide you in the strategies you select to help your child. The handouts on Frank's fears illustrate the different intervention strategies you may use. Remember, even if your child is facing a realistic fear, using strategies to calm the body (e.g., deep breathing) can still help.

We would then like you to distinguish between your child's realistic and unrealistic fears. We will review this worksheet **(My Child's Realistic and Unrealistic ["False Alarm"] Fears)** again next week.

Anxiety Components
A Fearful Experience at the Zoo

Heart racing, sweating, butterflies in stomach as you approach the snake cage

Physical reactions

Thoughts

The snake might get out of its cage!

Fewer opportunities to practice facing fears

Decreased learning and coping

Behaviors

Avoid the snake cage and/or the zoo

Parental Protection
The interaction between your parenting and your child's ability

Adaptive protection:

The child experiences situations as fearful. In many cases, these fears are realistic given the child's current skills. The parent provides appropriate protection based on the child's skill set.

The child experiences an anxiety-provoking situation.

The parent allows the child to face the fearful situation by knowing what the child can handle and when to encourage the child to face his or her fears given his or her skills.

The child faces his or her fears a little at a time when he or she is ready.

The child does not experience quite as much anxiety.

The parent gradually increases the child's exposure to the situation.

Excessive protection:

The child may have the necessary skills to handle him- or herself well in a potentially anxiety-producing situation, but the opportunity to face his or her fear is unnecessarily limited or prevented altogether. As a result, the child may continue to feel anxious in certain situations because of missed opportunities to develop coping strategies.

Child experiences an anxiety provoking situation

The parent allows the child to avoid the anxiety-provoking situation

Child does not practice coping skills

Graph of Anxiety Level Over Time

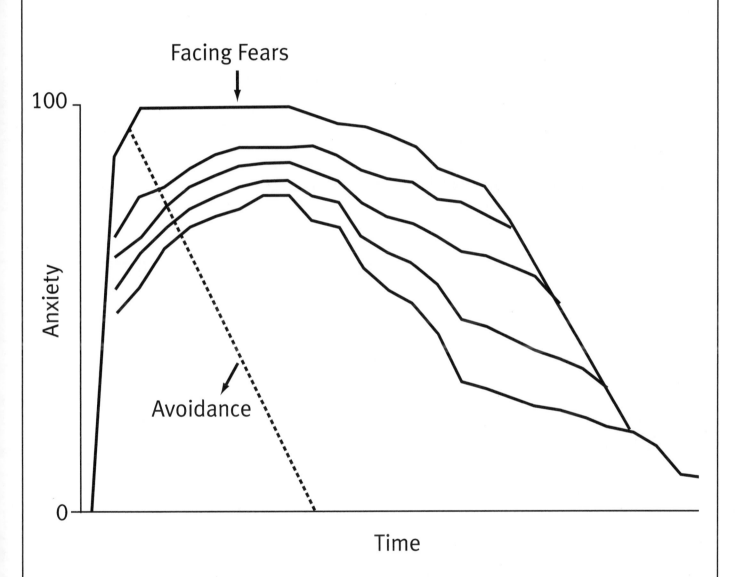

Frank's Fears
Realistic Versus Unrealistic ("False Alarm") Fears

Fears (circle the best response):

1. If I try out for the basketball team, then I might get cut.

   Realistic fear   Unrealistic fear

2. If I watch a scary movie, then the scary thoughts will never leave my head and bad things will happen.

   Realistic fear   Unrealistic fear

3. When I walk down the hall, kids may tease me.

   Realistic fear   Unrealistic fear

4. I'm struggling in math. If I don't study for the test, then I might fail.

   Realistic fear   Unrealistic fear

5. If I touch objects that other people touch, then I may get sick and die.

   Realistic fear   Unrealistic fear

6. If the news says there's a storm in the area, then there will be a tornado and something bad will happen.

   Realistic fear   Unrealistic fear

Frank's Realistic Fears

Realistic fears and interventions:

1. If I try out for the basketball team, then I might get cut.
   Determine why Frank wants to join the basketball team. If it is for social reasons, determine whether basketball is the best social outlet or if there are other social activities Frank might be better suited to participate in. If it is for the sport, determine whether Frank's skills are best suited for basketball or another sport. Help coach Frank in that sport.

2. When I walk down the hall, kids may tease me.
   Alert teachers to teasing in the hallway and request that they increase their monitoring. Allow Frank to leave class 5 minutes early to transition before the halls become crowded. Teach Frank to ignore teasing.

3. I'm struggling in math. If I don't study for the test, then I might fail.
   Provide Frank with study guides and a math tutor. Provide accommodations (e.g., extra time, reduce number of problems).

Frank's Unrealistic Fears
("False Alarms")

Unrealistic fears and interventions:

1. If I watch a scary movie, then the scary thoughts will never leave my head and bad things will happen.

2. If I touch objects that other people touch, then I may get sick and die.

3. If the news says there's a storm in the area, then there will be a tornado and something bad will happen.

Help Frank to identify the things that make him anxious. Teach Frank coping skills (i.e., tools to help him calm down). Gradually have Frank face his fears by progressing from his least feared situation to his most feared situation while coaching Frank to "use his tools." Reward courageous behavior. Remind Frank of the low probability that bad things will happen when he faces his fears. Over time, Frank will learn that he can handle the anxious feelings and that his anxiety goes down as he faces his fears.

My Child's Realistic and Unrealistic ("False Alarm") Fears

Realistic fears	Unrealistic fears
1.	1.
2.	2.
3.	3.
4.	4.
5.	5.

Session Notes

More Mind–Body Connections

Introduction to Exposure

44

Below is a worksheet your child will use to draw him- or herself relaxing.

Below, draw a picture of yourself relaxing.

What activity are you doing? How does your body feel? What are you thinking?

This Is Me Relaxing . . .

I'm thinking _____

I feel _____

The next set of worksheets illustrates how thoughts affect the body, and how the body's reaction can lead to negative thoughts and avoidant behaviors.

It's time to visit Matthew, the boy who is afraid of snakes, again. On the next page, you will see what happens to Matthew's body when he sees a snake at the zoo. His body alarm goes off, and his mind becomes active.

As Matthew begins to think more worried thoughts, his body alarm goes off even more!

After you read about Matthew, fill in your own **Alarm Chain Reaction** worksheet.

1. Pick a situation that makes you feel worried.

2. Write down how your body feels and what you think when you get worried.

Alarm Chain Reaction

Matthew sees a snake in a cage at the zoo . . . .

My Alarm Chain Reaction

Worry: _____

Physical feeling

Thoughts

1

2

3

Physical feeling

Thoughts

Physical feeling

Thoughts

Help out Matthew

Write down what he could do to help his body's alarm chain reaction.
(Hint: Make sure to include calming activities and helpful thoughts.
You can use the **Strategies for Calming Down and Facing Fears** worksheet.)

1. _____

_____

2. _____

_____

3. _____

_____

4. _____

_____

5. _____

_____

What Can I Do to Help Myself?

What could you do differently to help your body's alarm chain reaction?
(Hint: Make sure to include calming activities and helpful thoughts.
You can use the **Strategies for Calming Down and Facing Fears** worksheet.)

1. _____

_____

2. _____

_____

3. _____

_____

4. _____

_____

5. _____

_____

Strategies for Calming Down and Facing Fears

Suggestions for helpful thoughts:

- This is just a "false alarm."
- I can face my fear; nothing bad will happen.
- The worry feelings will go away.
- Fight back with facts.
- I can handle this.
- This is no big deal.
- Everyone makes mistakes.
- It's my worry bug; I can squash it!

Suggestions for calming activities:

- Take deep breaths.
- Go for a walk.
- Go outside.
- Ride my bike.
- Play with my pet.
- Read a book or magazine.
- Play video games.
- Watch television or a movie.
- Play with Lego set.
- Talk to someone.
- Play a game.
- Listen to music.
- Think about my favorite interest or activity.

Facing Fears Through Exposure

What is graded exposure? Graded exposure is the principle that gradual exposure to a feared situation or object will eventually reduce anxiety.

1. **Finding the target**

   • During the last session, you and your child used the stress-o-meter to select five fears and/or worries (or more) that interfere with your child's functioning at home or school or in the community (see examples) and listed them on the **Steps to Success: Finding My Target** worksheet. Looking at the fears and/or worries on that worksheet or on the **Fear Tracker** worksheet from the last session, ask your child which worry he or she would like to face first. Make sure the worry picked interferes with day-to-day functioning but that the anxiety is not so overwhelming to your child that he or she resists facing the fear. When completing the **Steps to Success: Finding My Target** worksheet, it is ok to have several fears listed at the same level (e.g., pretty big worry), rather than only listing one fear per level.

2. **Determining where to begin**

   • Using the **Steps to Success: Finding My Target** worksheet, take the target goal and create a series of steps that will lead to facing the fear. Write these steps from least anxiety producing (bottom of the ladder) to most anxiety producing (top of the ladder). It is sometimes helpful to identify the goal first and then, with your child, determine the small steps necessary to achieve the goal. All possible steps can be written separately on small cards and then put in order from easiest to hardest. This sequence can then be transferred to the **Steps to Success: Where Do We Begin?** worksheet.

   • Have your child select a reward that he or she will earn after facing his or her fear. You may provide mini rewards for each step of the ladder and a larger reward for completing all of the steps. Remember, you are rewarding effort in facing fears.

      • Help your child decide which strategies he or she will use as part of his or her plan. Write these down on the **Steps to Success: Where Do We Begin?** worksheet (see stress-o-meter). Examples include the following:

         • Handle your body's alarm reaction in an ongoing way (e.g., through exercise, deep breathing, and other calming activities).

(continued)

(continued)

Facing Fears Through Exposure

- Think helpful thoughts (e.g., "Fight back with facts," "I can do this," "The worry will go away").

- Take advice from your friends (e.g., read a book, watch television, think of all the animals you can that begin with *b,* use a fidget toy).

3. Practicing at home

- Select the lowest step on the ladder; remind your child that anxiety goes away over time and that exposure and practice is a powerful tool.

- Continue practicing the first step until your child indicates that he or she is ready to move to the next step. This may take a number of practices until he or she feels ready. Reward your child's efforts and/or progress on this step, and then go to the next step up the ladder.

- Be empathic and convey confidence in your child's ability to face fears! Acknowledge to your child that you know that it may be hard to face his or her fears but you know he or she can do it and you will be there to help.

- Review the strategies your child will use in his or her overall plan to help handle the anxiety he or she feels when faced with specific situations or objects.

- Remind your child that anxiety goes up and down and it is his or her job to move from the red zone to the yellow zone and the yellow zone to the green zone on his or her stress-o-meter.

- Remember to praise your child, but also help your child praise him- or herself.

- You are ready to begin!

Steps to Success: Finding My Target

Home alone
Biggest worry

Ordering food in a restaurant
Pretty big worry

Making mistakes
Medium worry

Toilets flushing
Bit of a worry

Dogs
Not much of a worry

Steps to Success: Finding My Target

Biggest worry

Pretty big worry

Medium worry

Bit of a worry

Not much of a worry

Steps to Success: Where Do We Begin?

What I'm working on (target goal): Making mistakes

What I'm working for (bigger reward!): Bionicles

My reward for every exposure practice will be (small reward): Piece of candy

I will practice facing my fears (how often?): Daily

(Begin with Step 1 and move to Step 6)

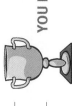

6. Make one mistake on a spelling test.

5. Make a mistake on math homework.

4. Make a mistake writing the date on homework, do not erase, and turn in.

3. Read a sentence out loud in small group and make a mistake with one of the words.

2. Make a mistake while writing your name, erase only once, and then turn in the paper.

1. Read a sentence out loud, and make a mistake reading one of the words in front of a parent.

Strategies for Success! What I can do to handle my worry and/or fear at home (e.g., deep breathing):

1. Tell myself I can handle this.

2. Tell myself that my body is having a "false alarm"!

3. Breathe deeply.

4. Tell myself that everyone makes mistakes. It is no big deal!

YOU DID IT!

Steps to Success: Where Do We Begin?

What I'm working on (target goal): Flushing toilet

What I'm working for (bigger reward!): Game boy game

My reward for every exposure practice will be (small reward): Piece of candy

I will practice facing my fears (how often?): Daily

(Begin with Step 1 and move to Step 6)

6. Go to a public bathroom and flush.

5. Stand by the toilet and flush.

4. Stand outside the stall while toilet flushes.

3. Stay in a public bathroom for 2 minutes.

2. Walk into a public bathroom for 1 minute.

1. Stand outside of a bathroom.

Strategies for Success! What I can do to handle my worry and/or fear at home (e.g., deep breathing):

1. Tell myself I can face this fear

2. Tell myself that my body is overreacting.

3. Breathe deeply.

4. Tell myself that toilets are loud but it does not mean anything bad will happen.

YOU DID IT!

Steps to Success: Where Do We Begin?

What I'm working on (target goal): *Ordering food in a restaurant*

What I'm working for (bigger reward!): *iTunes gift card*

My reward for every exposure practice will be (small reward): *A quarter*

I will practice facing my fears (how often?): *Daily*

(Begin with Step 1 and move to Step 6)

6. At a restaurant, order a Coke and all food items.

5. At a restaurant, order a Coke and one other food item; have parents order additional foods.

4. At a sit-down restaurant, order a Coke, and say, "I'll have this," pointing to the menu.

3. At a sit-down restaurant, order a Coke, and have parents order any other food.

2. Order a Coke inside McDonald's.

1. Order a Coke at the McDonald's drive-through.

Strategies for Success! What I can do to handle my worry and/or fear at home (e.g., deep breathing):

1. Tell myself I can face this fear.

2. Tell myself I'm having a "false alarm" reaction.

3. Breathe deeply.

4. Tell myself I'm just ordering food; it's no big deal.

YOU DID IT!

Steps to Success: Where Do We Begin?

What I'm working on (target goal): *Being alone in the house*

What I'm working for (bigger reward!): *Movie night*

My reward for every exposure practice will be (small reward): *A quarter*

I will practice facing my fears (how often?): *Daily*

(Begin with Step 1 and move to Step 6)

6. Stay in an upstairs room while Mom is in the basement for 5 minutes.

5. Stay in living room while Mom is up or down one level for 5 minutes.

4. Stay in living room while Mom is up or down one level for 3 minutes; call to her only one time.

3. Stand in the living room while Mom enters the adjoining kitchen; keep her in view.

2. Stand in the living room close to the doorway while Mom enters the adjoining kitchen.

1. Walk with Mom from living room to kitchen but don't stand next to her.

Strategies for Success! What I can do to handle my worry and/or fear at home (e.g., deep breathing):

1. Tell myself I can handle this.

2. Tell myself that my body is having a "false alarm"!

3. Breathe deeply.

4. Tell myself I can be away from Mom in the house—no problem!

YOU DID IT!

Session Notes

Introduction
to Exposure
(Continued)

Below is a worksheet the children will complete after each exposure.

SESSION 7

Facing Fears: How Did I Do?

1. How well did I face my fears?

2. How well did I use my tools?

3. What will I do differently next time? _____

_____

_____

Remember, look in your stress-o-meter to help you decide what to do next time!

Wow! Good job!

Below is information your child will need as he or she plans for his or her movie.

On the **Plan for My Movie** worksheet on the next page, you are going to choose your plot for your own movie!

Think about which of your worries you would like to target in your movie!

What will the steps to success be?
What will the plan be for calming down?
What will the reward be for facing your fear?
Where will your movie take place?
Who will the characters be?

Have fun planning your movie!

Plan for My Movie!

Specific worry or fear: _____

Steps to success
(facing fears a little at a time):

1. _____

2. _____

3. _____

4. _____

Strategies: (Hint: Make sure to include calming activities and helpful thoughts.)

_____

_____

_____

_____

REWARDS! _____

_____

Self-praise: _____

_____

Props: _____

_____

_____

Setting: _____

_____

Roles:

1. Fear Facer: _____

2. Coach: _____

3. Narrator: _____

4. Other: _____

Sample Script:
Facing Your Fears:_____

Narrator: Greetings. In our *Facing Your Fears* segment today, we are going to help you conquer your fear of _____. We will introduce you to _____, who is afraid of _____. To help _____ with his fear of _____, his friend _____ will coach him through the "steps to success." _____ will start with Step 1— _____
_____.

Child #1: Ok, I'm ready to face my fear of _____. I'll start by_____
_____.

Coach: Say, "I can do this—I want to beat this fear."

Child #1: I can do this. I want to beat this fear.

Coach: Where are you on your stress-o-meter?

Child #1: I'm starting to feel a little funny in my stomach; I think I'm at about a 6.

Coach: Try to get back down to a 4. Take a few deep breaths.

Child #1: (Takes a few breaths.)

Coach: Say, _____(provides suggestions for handling anxiety, such as helpful thoughts, and/or suggestions for calming/relaxing activities) _____
_____

Child #1: (Does suggestions) Now I think I am at about a 4.

Coach: Say, "I did it! Good for me, I finished the first step."

Child #1: I did it! Good for me, I finished the first step.

Narrator: (Child #1) _____'s next step is to _____
_____.

Child #1: I am ready to do the second step. I am ready to _____.
I'm starting to feel a little worried.

Coach: Tell yourself, "Oh, it's just my worry bug again. I can fight this."

Child #1: Oh, it's just my worry bug again. I can fight this, but I feel like I am at a 7. Ahhh, I don't know what to do!

(continued)

(continued)

Sample Script:
Facing Your Fears:_____

Coach: Take a few deep breaths.

Child #1: (Pauses and takes three deep breaths.)

Coach: You need to remember "helpful thoughts."

Child #1: I am strong. _____
(Thinks helpful thoughts, such as "fight back with facts," or task-neutral thoughts).
I know the worry feelings will go away. Hey, it's working. I feel better.

Narrator: (Child #1) _____'s next step is to _____
_____.

Child #1: I am ready to _____.
This is the hardest part, and I'm having trouble doing this! I feel like yelling.

Coach: Remember helpful thoughts. You can say, _____.
Tell yourself the worry feelings will go away.

Child #1: (Uses steps from plan.)

Child #1: I did it! I am proud of myself for not freaking out. I think I am at a 3.

Narrator: Now, (Child #1) _____'s final step is to _____.

Child #1: Now it's time for my final step. I am going to face my fear of _____ and
_____. Oh no, my worry is going up to an 8 this time.

Coach: Say, "I can do this." You need to calm yourself down. Take three deep breaths.

Child #1: I can do this. (Takes 3 deep breaths.) This will be over in a few minutes.

Child #1: I did it. I faced my fear of _____ and my worry passed. I did a good job!
I'm proud of myself. I think I'll reward myself with _____.

Coach: Great job! (High five.)

Narrator: Now, all of you have a plan for facing your fear of _____.
I'll see you next time on another episode of *Facing Your Fears!*

Session Notes

Practicing Exposure and Making Movies

Below is a worksheet that provides some guidance as your child films his or her movie.

Things to Think About While Filming Our Movies!

Goals

How are you doing on your *goals* at home?
Keep at it! You're doing great!

Relax and have fun

Are you planning fun activities and time to relax? Try to plan some fun things to do during the week and calming or relaxing activities.

Are you ready to *film* your movie?
Do you need props? What else do you need?

Filming

Have fun with your movies, and good luck with your goals at home!

Session Notes

Facing Fears and Making Movies

Facing Fears Rating Sheet

Name: _____

Session: _____

Date: _____

Fear: _____

Step to complete today in facing fears: _____

_____

Reward for exposure practice: _____

	Child anxiety rating	Parent rates child anxiety
Before exposure		
During exposure		
Immediately after exposure		
5 minutes after exposure		

Facing Fears: How Did I Do?

1. How well did I face my fears?

2. How well did I use my tools?

3. What will I do differently next time? _____

_____

_____

_____

Remember, look in your stress-o-meter to help you decide what to do next time!

Wow! Good job!

Session Notes

Facing Fears and Making Movies

Facing Fears Rating Sheet

Name: _____

Session: _____

Date: _____

Fear: _____

Step to complete today in facing fears: _____

_____

Reward for exposure practice: _____

	Child anxiety rating	Parent rates child anxiety
Before exposure		
During exposure		
Immediately after exposure		
5 minutes after exposure		

Facing Fears: How Did I Do?

1. How well did I face my fears?

2. How well did I use my tools?

3. What will I do differently next time?

_____

_____

_____

Remember, look in your stress-o-meter to help you decide what to do next time!

Wow! Good job!

Session Notes

Facing Fears
and Making Movies

Facing Fears Rating Sheet

Name: _____

Session: _____

Date: _____

Fear: _____

Step to complete today in facing fears: _____

_____

Reward for exposure practice: _____

	Child anxiety rating	Parent rates child anxiety
Before exposure		
During exposure		
Immediately after exposure		
5 minutes after exposure		

Facing Fears: How Did I Do?

1. How well did I face my fears?

2. How well did I use my tools?

3. What will I do differently next time?

Remember, look in your stress-o-meter to help you decide what to do next time!

Wow! Good job!

Session Notes

Facing Fears and Making Movies

Facing Fears Rating Sheet

Name: _____

Session: _____

Date: _____

Fear: _____

Step to complete today in facing fears: _____

_____

Reward for exposure practice: _____

	Child anxiety rating	Parent rates child anxiety
Before exposure		
During exposure		
Immediately after exposure		
5 minutes after exposure		

Facing Fears: How Did I Do?

1. How well did I face my fears?

 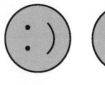

2. How well did I use my tools?

3. What will I do differently next time? _____

_____

_____

Remember, look in your stress-o-meter to help you decide what to do next time!

Wow! Good job!

Session Notes

Facing Fears and Making Movies

Facing Fears Rating Sheet

Name: _____

Session: _____

Date: _____

Fear: _____

Step to complete today in facing fears: _____

_____

Reward for exposure practice: _____

	Child anxiety rating	Parent rates child anxiety
Before exposure		
During exposure		
Immediately after exposure		
5 minutes after exposure		

Facing Fears: How Did I Do?

1. How well did I face my fears?

2. How well did I use my tools?

3. What will I do differently next time?

Remember, look in your stress-o-meter to help you decide what to do next time!

Wow! Good job!

Session Notes

Graduation

How Much Time Do You Spend Worrying Now?

Write down your worries here!

Fun time

Worry time

Time I spend worrying

Me

A little

Some

A lot!

My Favorite Tools

Calming and/or relaxing activities

_____

_____

_____

_____

Helpful thoughts

_____

_____

_____

_____

I faced fears by . . .

_____

_____

_____

_____

Lessons I Learned in Group

- We all use different words for worry—*scared, anxious, nervous,* and *freaked out* are some of them.

- When we worry too much, it can make it hard for us to have fun, do well in school, or get along with our family or friends.

- Different things make each of us worry or feel anxious. It may be a fear of the dark, of going outside, of staying home alone, or of talking to people.

- We can show worry or anxiety in lots of different ways, such as getting really quiet, leaving the room, crying, getting silly, or even having our bodies shake.

- Sometimes our worry is a "false alarm"—our bodies may feel upset, then our minds get really active and we start thinking all sorts of thoughts that make us worry more.

- It helps to know the kinds of situations that make us worry so we can get ready to fight it!

(continued)

(continued)

Lessons I Learned in Group

- We can do *lots* of things to get rid of worry. We can do relaxing and calming things like taking deep breaths, telling a joke, or going for a walk. We also can remember that helpful thoughts can make our bodies calm down. We can fight back with facts or tell ourselves that the worry feelings will go away. We can watch our favorite television shows, play video games, listen to music, ride bikes, read a book, or talk on the phone while we wait for our worry to go away.

- We are all very strong and tough. We can beat worry!

- Most important, we learned that the best way to get rid of worry is to face fears!

Favorite things I'll remember about my friends:

_____

_____

_____

_____

We learned a whole lot of different things in group!

Booster Session

Look at the **Stressed to Calm** worksheet and think of how the boy can solve a problem using helpful thoughts, calming and/or relaxing activities, and facing fears strategies to calm himself.

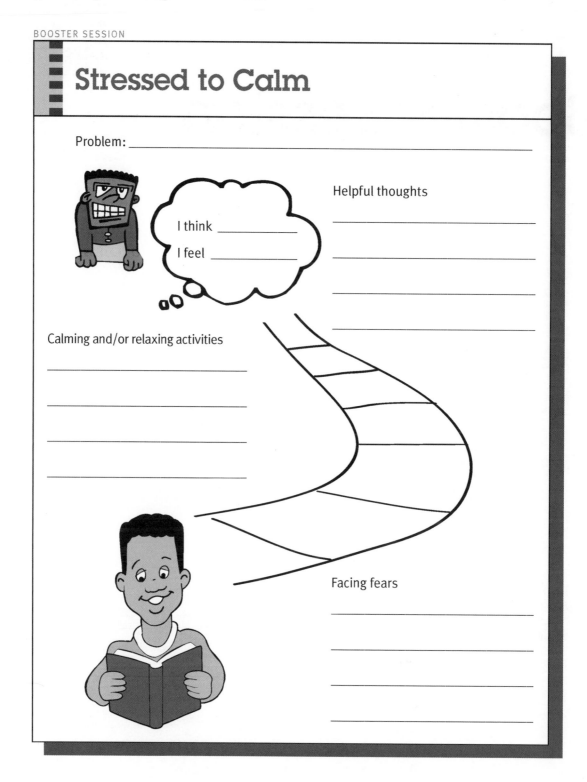

Session Notes